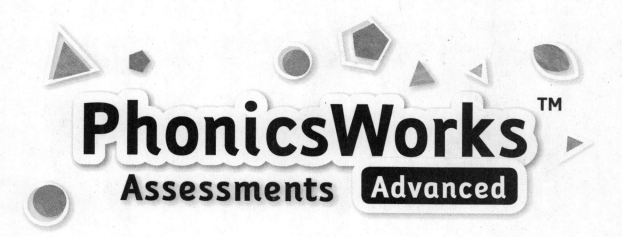

PhonicsWorks™
Assessments Advanced

Illustrations Credits
All illustrations © K12 unless otherwise noted

About K12 Inc.
K12 Inc. (NYSE: LRN) drives innovation and advances the quality of education by delivering state-of-the-art digital learning platforms and technology to students and school districts around the world. K12 is a company of educators offering its online and blended curriculum to charter schools, public school districts, private schools, and directly to families. More information can be found at K12.com.

978-1-60153-190-2
Printed by Action Printing, Fond du Lac, WI, USA, April 2019

Contents

Unit Checkpoint
Look Back: Sounds /ă/, /ŏ/, and /ŭ/ . . . . **PH 1**

Unit Checkpoint
Look Back: Sounds /ă/, /ĕ/, /ĭ/, /ŏ/, and /ŭ/ . . . . **PH 7**

Unit Checkpoint
Look Back: Digraphs *sh*, *ch*, and *th* . . . . **PH 13**

Unit Checkpoint
Look Back: Digraphs, Trigraphs, Sounds,
Letters, and Vowels . . . . **PH 19**

Unit Checkpoint
Ending Consonant Blends –*nd*, –*ft*, –*lk*,
and –*ct* . . . . **PH 25**

Unit Checkpoint
Ending Consonant Blends –*lp* and –*lt* . . . . **PH 31**

Unit Checkpoint
Ending Consonant Blends –*mp* and –*sp* . . . . . . **PH 37**

Unit Checkpoint
Ending Consonant Blends –*sk*, –*st*, –*nt*,
and –*nch* . . . . **PH 43**

Unit Checkpoint
Beginning Consonant Blends bl–, cl–, fl–,
gl–, pl–, and sl– ....PH 49

Unit Checkpoint
Beginning Consonant Blends br–, cr–, dr–,
fr–, gr–, pr–, and tr– ....PH 55

Unit Checkpoint
Beginning Digraph Blends shr– and thr– ......PH 61

Unit Checkpoint
Beginning Consonant Blends sc–, sp–, st–,
sw–, sk–, sm–, sn–, and tw– ....PH 67

Unit Checkpoint
Beginning Consonant Blends spr–, str–,
squ–, scr–, and spl–..........................PH 73

Unit Checkpoint
Words Ending in –ank, –ink, –onk,
and –unk ....PH 79

Unit Checkpoint
Words Ending in –ang, –ing, –ong,
and –ung ....PH 85

Unit Checkpoint
Silent e Spellings for Sounds /ā/, /ī/, /ō/, and /ē/ . . . . **PH 91**

Unit Checkpoint
Silent e Spellings for Sounds /ū/ and Long Double o . . . . **PH 97**

Unit Checkpoint
Sounds /ar/ & /or/, Beginning Blends, and Silent e Spellings . . . . **PH 103**

Unit Checkpoint
Contractions and Sound /z/ Spelled s . . . . **PH 109**

Unit Checkpoint
Two-Syllable Words and Schwa Sound . . . . **PH 115**

Unit Checkpoint
Endings –ing, –est, and –ed . . . . **PH 121**

Unit Checkpoint
Consonant Ending –le and Digraph ph . . . . **PH 127**

Unit Checkpoint
Spellings for Soft c and Soft g Sounds . . . . **PH 133**

Unit Checkpoint
Spellings for Sound /ā/ . . . . **PH 139**

Unit Checkpoint
Spellings for Sound /ī/ . . . . **PH 145**

Unit Checkpoint
Spellings for Sound /ō/ . . . . **PH 151**

Unit Checkpoint
Spellings for Sound /ē/ . . . . **PH 157**

Unit Checkpoint
Spellings for Sounds /ū/ and
Long Double o . . . . **PH 163**

Unit Checkpoint
Spellings for Double o Sounds . . . . **PH 169**

Unit Checkpoint
Review Long Vowels and
Double o Sounds . . . . **PH 175**

Unit Checkpoint
Sound /er/ Spelled –er, –ir, –ur, and –ear . . . . . **PH 181**

Unit Checkpoint
Sound /ĕ/ Spelled ea . . . . **PH 187**

Unit Checkpoint
Sound /oi/ Spelled oi and oy . . . . **PH 193**

Unit Checkpoint
    Sound /aw/ Spelled *au* and *aw*. . . . .**PH 199**

Unit Checkpoint
    Sound /ow/ Spelled *ou* and *ow*. . . . . **PH 205**

Unit Checkpoint
    Sound /ō/ Spelled *ow* . . . .**PH 211**

Unit Checkpoint
Look Back: Sounds /ă/, /ě/, /ĭ/, /ŏ/, and /ŭ/

Part 1. Read Words and Word Parts

Read across the row from left to right. Say the sounds of the word or word part.

1. –en	**2.** –un	**3.** it
4. at	**5.** an	**6.** –ig
7. am	**8.** –ob	**9.** –ip
10. –ut	**11.** –et	**12.** –ap
13. –ed	**14.** on	**15.** –im

Part 2. Finger Stretching

Listen to the word. Finger stretch the word.

16.

17.

18.

19.

20.

21.

22.

23.

24.

25.

26.

27.

PHONICS

Part 3. Dictation

Listen to the word. Repeat the word, and then write it.

28. _____

29. _____

30. _____

31. _____

32. _____

33. _____

Part 4. Writing

Listen to the sentence. Repeat the sentence, and then write it.

PHONICS

34. _____

35. _____

Part 5. Read Aloud

Read the sentences aloud.

36. They both went to the cab.

37. Bob has a mug for you.

38. Where is Ted from?

39. There is the big red dog.

40. Did you have fun? Yes, we did!

Part 6. Say Letters

Listen to the sound. Say the letter that makes that sound.

41.

42.

43.

44.

45.

46.

47.

48.

49.

Unit Checkpoint
Look Back: Digraphs *sh*, *ch*, and *th*

Part 1. Read Letters and Word Parts

Read across the row from left to right. Say the sounds of the letter or word part.

1. –ish	2. –eth	3. –all
4. –uth	5. i	6. –oth
7. a	8. –ith	9. o
10. –ash	11. –ush	12. –ach
13. e	14. –uch	15. u

Part 2. Finger Stretching

Listen to the word. Finger stretch the word.

16.

17.

18.

19.

20.

21.

PHONICS

Part 3. Dictation

Listen to the word. Repeat the word, and then write it.

22. _____

23. _____

24. _____

25. _____

26. _____

27. _____

PHONICS

Part 4. Writing

Listen to the sentence. Repeat the sentence, and then write it.

28. _____

29. _____

Part 5. Read Aloud

Read the sentences aloud.

30. Their dad said yes.

31. What did Jeff want with Chip?

32. Did you see who ran into the log?

33. I will miss her.

34. She had your dish.

Part 6. Say Letters

Listen to the sound. Say the letter or letters that make that sound.

35.	38.	41.
36.	39.	42.
37.	40.	43.

PHONICS

Unit Checkpoint
Look Back: Digraphs, Trigraphs, Sounds, Letters, and Vowels

Part 1. Read Words and Word Parts

Read across the row from left to right. Say the sounds of the word or word part.

1. itch	**2.** –ock	**3.** wi–
4. –ach	**5.** –osh	**6.** –uch
7. ash	**8.** –uth	**9.** –ith
10. –ak	**11.** wa–	**12.** –ech

Part 2. Finger Stretching

Listen to the word. Finger stretch the word.

13.

14.

15.

16.

PHONICS

Part 3. Dictation

Listen to the word. Repeat the word, and then write it.

17. _____

18. _____

19. _____

20. _____

21. _____

22. _____

23. _____

24. _____

PHONICS

PHONICS

Part 4. Writing

Listen to the sentence. Repeat the sentence, and then write it.

25. _____

26. _____

27. _____

Part 5. Read Aloud

Read the sentences aloud.

28. Dr. Nash has to check on Nick.

29. Where were you?

30. Chuck had to dig the ditches.

31. My pals are fun.

32. Why does that one latch?

PHONICS

Part 6. Say Letters

Listen to the sound. Say the letter or letters that make that sound.

33.

34.

35.

36.

37.

38.

39.

40.

PHONICS

Unit Checkpoint
Ending Consonant Blends —*nd*, —*ft*, —*lk*, and —*ct*

Part 1. Read Words and Word Parts

Read across the row from left to right. Say the sounds of the word or word part.

1. act	**2.** –ict	**3.** –uct
4. –oct	**5.** –aft	**6.** –uft
7. –eft	**8.** –ift	**9.** –oft
10. –ulk	**11.** –ilk	**12.** elk
13. –ond	**14.** –und	**15.** and
16. end	**17.** –uff	**18.** ill

Part 2. Finger Stretching

Listen to the word. Finger stretch the word.

PHONICS

19.

20.

21.

22.

23.

24.

25.

26.

Part 3. Dictation

Listen to the word. Repeat the word, and then write it.

27. _____

28. _____

29. _____

30. _____

31. _____

32. _____

PHONICS

PHONICS

Part 4. Writing

Listen to the sentence. Repeat the sentence, and then write it.

33. _____

34. _____

LANGUAGE ARTS GREEN | ENDING CONSONANT BLENDS *–nd, –ft, –lk,* AND *–ct*

Part 5. Read Aloud

Read the sentences aloud.

35.

Is the gift in the box?

I left the milk in the cup.

I will walk to the silk shop.

The sand is wet at the pond.

Beth will talk to Kim, too.

Part 6. Say Letters

Listen to the sound. Say the letter or letters that make that sound.

36.	42.	48.
37.	43.	49.
38.	44.	50.
39.	45.	51.
40.	46.	52.
41.	47.	53.

Unit Checkpoint
Ending Consonant Blends *–lp* and *–lt*

Part 1. Read Words and Word Parts

Read across the row from left to right. Say the sounds of the word or word part.

1. –elt	**2.** –ilt	**3.** elk
4. alp	**5.** –elp	**6.** –ulp
7. –ift	**8.** –oft	**9.** –ulk
10. –ilk	**11.** –ond	**12.** –und
13. and	**14.** end	**15.** act

Part 2. Finger Stretching

Listen to the word. Finger stretch the word.

16. _____

17. _____

18. _____

19. _____

20. _____

21. _____

PHONICS

Part 3. Dictation

Listen to the word. Repeat the word, and then write it.

22. _____

23. _____

24. _____

25. _____

26. _____

27. _____

Part 4. Writing

Listen to the sentence. Repeat the sentence, and then write it.

28. _____

29. _____

Name   Date

Part 5. Read Aloud

Read the sentences aloud.

30.

> Hand me the felt belt.
>
> I can help you fix the van again.
>
> Did you gulp all the milk?
>
> Pull out the big quilt.
>
> Did the top tilt on its end?

PHONICS

Part 6. Say Letters

Listen to the sound. Say the letter or letters that make that sound.

31.   34.   37.

32.   35.   38.

33.   36.   39.

PHONICS

Unit Checkpoint
Ending Consonant Blends –*mp* and –*sp*

Part 1. Read Word Parts

Read across the row from left to right. Say the sounds of the word part.

1. –elt	**2.** –imp	**3.** –omp
4. –asp	**5.** –usp	**6.** –osp
7. –ump	**8.** –amp	**9.** –ilk
10. –oft	**11.** –and	**12.** –act
13. –ith	**14.** –ush	**15.** –ich

Part 2. Finger Stretching

Listen to the word. Finger stretch the word.

16.

17.

18.

19.

20.

21.

22.

23.

Part 3. Dictation

Listen to the word. Repeat the word, and then write it.

24. _____

25. _____

26. _____

27. _____

28. _____

29. _____

Part 4. Writing

Listen to the sentence. Repeat the sentence, and then write it.

PHONICS

30. _____

31. _____

Part 5. Read Aloud

Read the sentences aloud.

32.

> She will jump into the pond.
>
> Your chimp is a champ.
>
> Bob had to gasp when he ran fast.
>
> Can you lend me a hand?

Part 6. Say Letters

Listen to the sound. Say the letter or letters that make that sound.

33.

34.

35.

36.

37.

38.

39.

40.

41.

Unit Checkpoint
Ending Consonant Blends −*sk*, −*st*, −*nt*, and −*nch*

Part 1. Read Word Parts

Read across the row from left to right. Say the sounds of the word part.

1. −ask	2. −unch	3. −ast
4. −est	5. −ant	6. −unt
7. −anch	8. −imp	9. −esk
10. −ust	11. −int	12. −onch
13. −inch	14. −ond	15. −isk

PHONICS

Part 2. Finger Stretching

Listen to the word. Finger stretch the word.

16.

17.

18.

19.

20.

21.

22.

23.

Part 3. Dictation

Listen to the word. Repeat the word, and then write it.

24. _____

25. _____

26. _____

27. _____

28. _____

29. _____

Part 4. Writing

Listen to the sentence. Repeat the sentence, and then write it.

30. _____

31. _____

Part 5. Read Aloud

Read the sentences aloud.

32.

> Did you ask for the red vest?
>
> We sent my friend back to the tent.
>
> We must have lunch on this bench.
>
> Am I next?
>
> Did the chicks hatch on a ranch?

Part 6. Say Letters

Listen to the sound. Say the letter or letters that make that sound.

33.	36.	39.
34.	37.	40.
35.	38.	41.

Unit Checkpoint
Beginning Consonant Blends *bl–*, *cl–*, *fl–*, *gl–*, *pl–*, and *sl–*

Part 1. Read Nonsense Words

Read across the row from left to right. Say the sounds of the nonsense word.

1. blap	**2.** clin	**3.** glom
4. plam	**5.** slod	**6.** flim
7. blek	**8.** clag	**9.** glup
10. plup	**11.** slan	**12.** flom
13. blop	**14.** ond	**15.** isk

Part 2. Finger Stretching

Listen to the word. Finger stretch the word.

16.

17.

18.

19.

20.

21.

Part 3. Dictation

Listen to the word. Repeat the word, and then write it.

22. _____

23. _____

24. _____

25. _____

26. _____

27. _____

Part 4. Writing

Listen to the sentence. Repeat the sentence, and then write it.

PHONICS

28. _____

29. _____

Part 5. Read Aloud

Read the sentences aloud.

30.

We had a blast at lunch.

Are there plans to do anything with Mr. Fletch?

The flag will begin to flap in the wind.

Cliff is glad he goes to class.

PHONICS

Part 6. Say Letters

Listen to the sound. Say the letter or letters that make that sound.

31.	34.	37.
32.	35.	38.
33.	36.	39.

Unit Checkpoint
Beginning Consonant Blends *br–*, *cr–*, *dr–*, *fr–*, *gr–*, *pr–*, and *tr–*

Part 1. Read Nonsense Words

Read across the row from left to right. Say the sounds of the nonsense word.

1. brazz	2. crin	3. drob
4. frup	5. grix	6. preff
7. triv	8. blass	9. klig
10. glud	11. ploc	12. sleg
13. thig	14. quib	15. wob

Part 2. Finger Stretching

Listen to the word. Finger stretch the word.

16.

17.

18.

19.

20.

21.

Part 3. Dictation

Listen to the word. Repeat the word, and then write it.

22. _____

23. _____

24. _____

25. _____

26. _____

27. _____

Part 4. Writing

Listen to the sentence. Repeat the sentence, and then write it.

28. _____

29. _____

Part 5. Read Aloud

Read the sentences aloud.

30.

> The frogs begin to hop in the grass.
>
> The crab shell goes in the trash.
>
> Dad put hot dogs on the grill.
>
> The trams go on this track.
>
> My friend has a black and red dress.

Part 6. Say Letters

Listen to the sound. Say the letter or letters that make that sound.

31.	34.	37.
32.	35.	38.
33.	36.	39.

Unit Checkpoint
Beginning Digraph Blends *shr–* and *thr–*

Part 1. Read Nonsense Words

Read across the row from left to right. Say the sounds of the nonsense word.

1. shrim	**2.** shrob	**3.** thrug
4. threx	**5.** shrap	**6.** thriz
7. trad	**8.** blas	**9.** frip
10. prud	**11.** ploc	**12.** slep
13. thig	**14.** quib	**15.** wib

Part 2. Finger Stretching

Listen to the word. Finger stretch the word.

16.

17.

18.

19.

Part 3. Dictation

Listen to the word. Repeat the word, and then write it.

20. _____

21. _____

22. _____

23. _____

24. _____

25. _____

Part 4. Writing

Listen to the sentence. Repeat the sentence, and then write it.

26. _____

27. _____

Part 5. Read Aloud

Read the sentences aloud.

28.

> "I know I am after you," said Beth.
>
> It was a thrill to drum in the band.
>
> The shrill thrush is down in the shrub.

Part 6. Say Letters

Listen to the sound. Say the letter or letters that make that sound.

29.   32.   35.

30.   33.   36.

31.   34.   37.

Unit Checkpoint
Beginning Consonant Blends *sc–*, *sp–*, *st–*, *sw–*, *sk–*, *sm–*, *sn–*, and *tw–*

PHONICS

Part 1. Read Nonsense Words

Read across the row from left to right. Say the sounds of the nonsense word.

1. skox	**2.** spich	**3.** stath	**4.** swed	**5.** skib
6. snosh	**7.** twik	**8.** shrip	**9.** thram	**10.** trib

Part 2. Finger Stretching

Listen to the word. Finger stretch the word.

11.

12.

13.

14.

15.

16.

17.

18.

Part 3. Dictation

Listen to the word. Repeat the word, and then write it.

19. _____

20. _____

21. _____

22. _____

23. _____

24. _____

25. _____

26. _____

PHONICS

Part 4. Writing

Listen to the sentence. Repeat the sentence, and then write it.

PHONICS

27. _____

28. _____

29. _____

Part 5. Read Aloud

Read the sentences aloud.

30.

Father has a spot on his scalp.

A twig is only a stick.

Did Mother step on the stump?

Two fish swim and swish.

The small twins snip the quilt.

Part 6. Say Letters

Listen to the sound. Say the letter that makes that sound.

31.	**34.**	**37.**
32.	**35.**	**38.**
33.	**36.**	**39.**

PHONICS

Unit Checkpoint
Beginning Consonant Blends *spr–*, *str–*, *squ–*, *scr–*, and *spl–*

Part 1. Read Nonsense Words

Read across the row from left to right. Say the sounds of the nonsense word.

1. splof	**2.** splok	**3.** spran	**4.** sprut	**5.** streb
6. skrush	**7.** skrad	**8.** squip	**9.** squix	**10.** twib

Part 2. Finger Stretching

Listen to the word. Finger stretch the word.

11.

12.

13.

14.

Part 3. Dictation

Listen to the word. Repeat the word, and then write it.

15. _____

16. _____

17. _____

18. _____

19. _____

20. _____

21. _____

22. _____

Part 4. Writing

Listen to the sentence. Repeat the sentence, and then write it.

23. _____

24. _____

25. _____

Part 5. Read Aloud

Read the sentences aloud.

26.

I lost the strap for my backpack.

A squid has ten legs.

Mr. Twig can scrub the bathtub.

Can Scott stretch the strand?

It is spring at last!

PHONICS

Part 6. Say Letters

Listen to the sound. Say the letter that makes that sound.

27.   30.   33.

28.   31.   34.

29.   32.   35.

PHONICS

Unit Checkpoint
Words Ending in *–ank*, *–ink*, *–onk*, and *–unk*

Part 1. Read Word Parts and Nonsense Words

Read across the row from left to right. Say the sound or sounds of the word part or nonsense word.

1. –ank	**2.** –ink	**3.** –onk	**4.** –unk	**5.** spap
6. stid	**7.** swib	**8.** skon	**9.** smep	**10.** snux

Part 2. Finger Stretching

Listen to the word. Finger stretch the word.

11.

12.

13.

14.

15.

16.

17.

18.

Part 3. Dictation

Listen to the word. Repeat the word, and then write it.

19. _____

20. _____

21. _____

22. _____

23. _____

24. _____

25. _____

26. _____

Part 4. Writing

Listen to the sentence. Repeat the sentence, and then write it.

PHONICS

27. _____

28. _____

29. _____

Part 5. Read Aloud

Read the sentences aloud.

30.

Only Mother has gone to the bank.

I even drank my drink.

I think my pants shrank.

Frank has a bunk bed.

Unit Checkpoint
Words Ending in –*ang*, –*ing*, –*ong*, and –*ung*

Part 1. Read Word Parts and Nonsense Words

Read across the row from left to right. Say the sound or sounds of the word part or nonsense word.

1. –ang	**2.** –ing	**3.** –ong	**4.** –ung
5. –ank	**6.** –ink	**7.** –onk	**8.** –unk
9. spog	**10.** shrid	**11.** drob	**12.** frug

Part 2. Finger Stretching

Listen to the word. Finger stretch the word.

13.

14.

15.

16.

Part 3. Dictation

Listen to the word. Repeat the word, and then write it.

17. _____

18. _____

19. _____

20. _____

21. _____

22. _____

23. _____

24. _____

PHONICS

Part 4. Writing

Listen to the sentence. Repeat the sentence, and then write it.

25. _____

26. _____

27. _____

Part 5. Read Aloud

Read the sentences aloud.

28.

They love to sing long songs.

Six bells ring. Ding dong!

We hung some pins on the string.

The sting was very bad for him.

Part 6. Say Letters

Listen to the sound. Say the letters that make that sound.

29.

30.

31.

32.

33.

34.

35.

Unit Checkpoint
Silent *e* Spellings for Sounds /ā/, /ī/, /ō/, and /ē/

Part 1. Read Words and Word Parts

Read across the row from left to right. Say the sound or sounds of the word or word part.

1. ate	**2.** –ap	**3.** –afe	**4.** –ine
5. –ipe	**6.** –ike	**7.** –ete	**8.** eve
9. ode	**10.** –ope	**11.** –ing	**12.** –unk

Part 2. Finger Stretching

Listen to the word. Finger stretch the word.

13.

14.

15.

16.

Part 3. Dictation

Listen to the word. Repeat the word, and then write it.

17. _____

18. _____

19. _____

20. _____

21. _____

22. _____

23. _____

24. _____

Part 4. Writing

Listen to the sentence. Repeat the sentence, and then write it.

25. _____

26. _____

27. _____

Part 5. Read Aloud

Read the sentences aloud.

28.

> Dad will bake a cake.
>
> Who left these white stones here?
>
> There is some time left for Steve.
>
> What is your name?
>
> We rode the bikes for five miles.

PHONICS

Part 6. Say Letters

Listen to the word part. Say the letters that make that word part.

29.	33.
30.	34.
31.	35.
32.	

Unit Checkpoint
Silent *e* Spellings for Sounds /ū/ and Long Double *o*

Part 1. Read Words and Word Parts

Read across the row from left to right. Say the sound or sounds of the word or word part.

1. –uke	**2.** –ule	**3.** up
4. us	**5.** –ane	**6.** –ike
7. –ete	**8.** –ave	**9.** –ode
10. –ope	**11.** –ing	**12.** –unk

Part 2. Finger Stretching

Listen to the word. Finger stretch the word.

13.

14.

15.

16.

Part 3. Dictation

Listen to the word. Repeat the word, and then write it.

17. _____

18. _____

19. _____

20. _____

21. _____

22. _____

23. _____

24. _____

Part 4. Writing

Listen to the sentence. Repeat the sentence, and then write it.

25. _____

26. _____

27. _____

Part 5. Read Aloud

Read the sentences aloud.

28.
> The pup is cute.
>
> He held the flute.
>
> Who broke the rule?
>
> None of us went to camp last June.
>
> We want to use more.
>
> A cube has six sides.

Part 6. Say Letters

Listen to the word part. Say the letters that make that word part.

29.

30.

31.

32.

33.

34.

35.

Unit Checkpoint
Sounds /ar/ & /or/, Beginning Blends, and Silent *e* Spellings

Part 1. Read Word Parts

Read across the row from left to right. Say the sound or sounds of the word part.

1. –arp	**2.** –ort	**3.** –isp
4. –ank	**5.** –ine	**6.** cor–
7. –ute	**8.** –ake	**9.** var–
10. stig–	**11.** –obe	**12.** snop–

Part 2. Finger Stretching

Listen to the word. Finger stretch the word.

13.

14.

Part 3. Dictation

Listen to the word. Repeat the word, and then write it.

15. _____

16. _____

17. _____

18. _____

19. _____

20. _____

21. _____

22. _____

Part 4. Writing

Listen to the sentence. Repeat the sentence, and then write it.

PHONICS

23. _____

24. _____

25. _____

Part 5. Read Aloud

Read the sentences aloud.

26.

> Smith Farm is six miles from Blane Park.
>
> Would you print your name on the form?
>
> That flat stone should skip far.
>
> Steve could make us a fort.

PHONICS

Part 6. Say Letters

Listen to the sound. Say the letters that make that sound.

27.

28.

29.

30.

31.

32.

33.

Unit Checkpoint
Contractions and Sound /z/ Spelled *s*

Part 1. Count Sounds

Count the number of sounds in the word and write the number.

1. rose _____

2. as _____

3. chase _____

4. case _____

5. rise _____

6. base _____

Part 2. Matching
Draw a line to match the words to their contraction.

7. is not   can't

8. did not   wasn't

9. has not   aren't

10. can not   hasn't

11. was not   didn't

12. are not   isn't

Part 3. Sound /z/ or /s/ Spelled s

Read the word aloud. Write s if the word ends with the sound /s/. Write z if the word ends with the sound /z/.

13. rose _____

14. nose _____

15. chase _____

16. base _____

17. rise _____

18. case _____

Part 4. Writing

Listen to the sentence. Repeat the sentence, and then write it.

19. _____

20. _____

21. _____

Part 5. Read Aloud

Read the sentences aloud.

22.

Her nose isn't so red.

The rose wasn't in the vase.

Aren't the bases in the case?

Let's ask the wise man.

Mrs. Prose didn't close the gate.

He can't fix the fuse box.

Mr. Smith wants only those grapes.

Where is Mrs. Muzz?

Part 6. Read Words

Read each word aloud.

23. case	**24.** nose	**25.** sunrise
26. hose	**27.** roses	**28.** baseball

Part 7. Read Nonsense Words

Read each nonsense word aloud.

29. pote	**30.** fise	**31.** hing
32. fonk	**33.** strug	**34.** vobe
35. wux	**36.** zune	**37.** pise
38. biss		

Unit Checkpoint
Two-Syllable Words and Schwa Sound

Part 1. Count Syllables

Count the number of syllables in the word and write the number.

1. radish _____

2. fantastic _____

3. pumpkin _____

4. basket _____

5. mitten _____

6. kitten _____

Part 2. Vowel or Consonant

Listen to the letter. If it's a vowel, write the letter in the first column. If it's a consonant, write the letter in the second column.

	Vowel	Consonant
7.	_____	_____
8.	_____	_____
9.	_____	_____
10.	_____	_____

Part 3. True or False

Listen to each statement. Write *T* if the statement is true and *F* if the statement is false.

11. Every word has at least one syllable. _____

12. Every syllable has one vowel sound. _____

Part 4. Writing

Listen to the sentence. Repeat the sentence, and then write it.

PHONICS

13. _____

14. _____

15. _____

Part 5. Read Aloud

Read the sentences aloud.

16.

> Ellen put a pink ribbon on the basket of muffins.
>
> Miles has seven buttons in his pocket.
>
> The alarm was so shrill I awoke with a start.
>
> I went to the doctor after the hornet stung me.
>
> Mom made red velvet cupcakes.

Part 6. Say Sounds

Listen to the syllables in the word. Say which syllable has the schwa sound.

17.   18.   19.

20.   21.   22.

Unit Checkpoint
Endings *–ing*, *–est*, and *–ed*

Part 1. Count Syllables

Count the number of syllables in the word and write the number.

1. biggest _____

2. smartest _____

3. softest _____

4. quickest _____

5. hardest _____

6. sudden _____

Part 2. Identify Ending Sounds

Listen to the word. Decide if the word ends with the sound /ed/, /d/, or /t/. Write *ed*, *d*, or *t* and read the word aloud.

7. hopped _____   8. jumped _____

9. trusted _____   10. stalled _____

11. slammed _____   12. acted _____

Part 3. Read Sight Words

Read each sight word aloud.

13. many

14. animal

15. while

16. sister

17. more

18. would

19. baby

20. brother

Part 4. Writing

Listen to the sentence. Repeat the sentence, and then write it.

21. _____

22. _____

23. _____

_____

Part 5. Read Aloud
Read the sentences aloud.

24.

Where did they go fishing?

She wanted to catch the biggest sunfish.

He printed his name.

They clapped their hands the fastest.

How many animals are there?

PHONICS

Part 6. Read Words

Read each word aloud.

25. zipped	**26.** batted
27. chopped	**28.** filled
29. pecking	**30.** patching
31. batting	**32.** softest

PHONICS

Unit Checkpoint
Consonant Ending –le and Digraph ph

Part 1. Count Syllables

Count the number of syllables in the word and write the number.

1. bubble _____

2. simple _____

3. apple _____

4. jingle _____

5. little _____

6. marble _____

PHONICS

Part 2. Vowel or Consonant

Listen to the letter. If it's a vowel, write the letter in the first column. If it's a consonant, write the letter in the second column.

Vowel	Consonant
7. _____	_____
8. _____	_____
9. _____	_____
10. _____	_____

Part 3. True or False

Listen to each statement. Write *T* if the statement is true and *F* if the statement is false.

11. Every syllable has only one vowel sound. _____

12. The letters *ph* spell the sound /f/. _____

Part 4. Writing

Listen to the sentence. Repeat the sentence, and then write it.

13. _____

14. _____

15. _____

Part 5. Read Aloud

Read the sentences aloud.

16.

Uncle Phil lit the candle.

This puzzle is very hard.

I know how to juggle.

I saw a very small pebble.

The animal I like best is the elephant.

Part 6. Read Sight Words

Read each sight word aloud.

17. many	**18.** animals	**19.** while
20. mother	**21.** father	**22.** brother
23. sister	**24.** baby	**25.** only
26. friend		

Unit Checkpoint
Spellings for Soft *c* and Soft *g* Sounds

Part 1. Circle Words with Sound /j/

Circle all the words in which the g spells the sound /j/.

1. page
2. brag
3. large
4. gem
5. huge
6. gaggle
7. gentle
8. cage

Part 2. Circle Words with Sound /s/

Circle all the words in which the c spells the sound /s/.

9. cape 10. cite 11. place 12. clap

13. cent 14. cage 15. cold 16. prance

Part 3. Read Sight Words

Read each sight word aloud.

17. other	**18.** people	**19.** together
20. many	**21.** animals	**22.** while
23. would	**24.** know	

Part 4. Writing

Listen to the sentence. Repeat the sentence, and then write it.

25. _____

_____

26. _____

27. _____

PHONICS

Part 5. Read Aloud

Read the sentences aloud.

28.

> The fridge would not budge.
>
> I want some of that nice fudge in a while.
>
> This gadget does not work.
>
> The judge is working at his bench.
>
> Most people will want to go together.

Part 6. Read Words

Read each word aloud.

29. space	**30.** dodged	**31.** edge
32. fidgeting	**33.** bridge	**34.** circus
35. gentle	**36.** page	

PHONICS

Unit Checkpoint
Spellings for Sound /ā/

PHONICS

Part 1. Circle Words with Sound /ā/

Circle all the words that have the long a sound.

1. dame   2. back   3. plain   4. tray

5. apple   6. weigh   7. raven   8. past

Part 2. Many Spellings, One Sound

Circle the five ways to spell the long a sound.

9. a-e   **10.** ao   **11.** a   **12.** eigh

13. aw   **14.** ay   **15.** ai   **16.** au

Part 3. Read Sight Words

Read each sight word aloud.

17. move   **18.** people   **19.** while

20. here   **21.** together   **22.** other

23. many   **24.** know

Part 4. Writing

Listen to the sentence. Repeat the sentence, and then write it.

25. _____

26. _____

27. _____

Part 5. Read Aloud

Read the sentences aloud.

28.

David's chipmunk has the acorn.

Move the pail that is above you.

Put my lunch here on this tray.

Sit on that chair so I can braid your hair.

This train weighs more than eight cars.

Part 6. Read Nonsense Words

Read each nonsense word aloud.

29. paip	**30.** chame	**31.** tay	**32.** peight
33. vable	**34.** daib	**35.** phay	**36.** craid

Part 7. Read Words

Read each word aloud.

37. data	**38.** play	**39.** pain	**40.** snail
41. weight	**42.** sleigh	**43.** basic	**44.** tray

Unit Checkpoint
Spellings for Sound /ī/

Part 1. Circle Words with Sound /ī/

Circle all the words that have the long *i* sound.

1. spike   2. pill   3. fly   4. pie

5. right   6. find   7. lick   8. silent

Part 2. Many Spellings, One Sound

Circle the five ways to spell the long *i* sound.

9. i-e   **10.** ei   **11.** igh   **12.** ai

13. i   **14.** ay   **15.** ie   **16.** y

Part 3. Read Sight Words
Read each sight word aloud.

17. above   **18.** here   **19.** move

20. other   **21.** people   **22.** together

23. many   **24.** while

Part 4. Writing

Listen to the sentence. Repeat the sentence, and then write it.

25. _____

26. _____

27. _____

Part 5. Read Aloud

Read the sentences aloud.

28.

> The silent child is quite shy.
>
> Why did you decide to fly that biplane?
>
> Lightning was in the sky and it struck the pines.
>
> David will try to make a fine pie.
>
> Some people are not kind and they tell lies.

Part 6. Read Nonsense Words

Read each nonsense word aloud.

29. zigh	**30.** chy	**31.** bry	**32.** pight
33. bife	**34.** gite	**35.** nild	**36.** ki

Unit Checkpoint
Spellings for Sound /ō/

Part 1. Circle Words with Sound /ō/

Circle all the words that have the long o sound.

1. choke   **2.** slow   **3.** hop   **4.** doe

5. told   **6.** cot   **7.** coat   **8.** frozen

Part 2. Many Spellings, One Sound

Circle the five ways to spell the long o sound.

9. oa   **10.** oo   **11.** o   **12.** oy

13. ow   **14.** o-e   **15.** ou   **16.** oe

Part 3. Read Sight Words

Read each sight word aloud.

17. these   **18.** against   **19.** now   **20.** above

---

21. here   **22.** move   **23.** other   **24.** people

Part 4. Writing

Listen to the sentence. Repeat the sentence, and then write it.

25. _____

26. _____

_____

27. _____

Part 5. Read Aloud

Read the sentences aloud.

28.

> Could you hold these old coats for me?
>
> He told you to hoe against that big row.
>
> We got our goldfish the biggest glass bowl.
>
> Let's throw snowballs at that target!
>
> Now follow me to the sailboat.

Part 6. Read Nonsense Words

Read each nonsense word aloud.

29. yone	**30.** oach	**31.** voe	**32.** trow
33. pho	**34.** fost	**35.** ploe	**36.** zow

PHONICS

Unit Checkpoint
Spellings for Sound /ē/

Part 1. Circle Words with Sound /ē/

Circle all the words that have the long e sound.

1. piece   2. frosty   3. speaking   4. send

5. stretch   6. be   7. eighteen   8. Pete

PHONICS

Part 2. Many Spellings, One Sound

Circle the six ways to spell the long e sound.

9. ee   **10.** oe   **11.** ie   **12.** y

13. ea   **14.** e-e   **15.** ew   **16.** e

Part 3. Read Sight Words

Read each sight word aloud.

17. every   **18.** neighbor   **19.** behind   **20.** these

21. against   **22.** now   **23.** above   **24.** here

Part 4. Writing

Listen to the sentence. Repeat the sentence, and then write it.

25. _____

26. _____

27. _____

_____

Part 5. Read Aloud

Read the sentences aloud.

28.

> Did you see the baby chimpanzee?
>
> Brush your teeth every night before you go to sleep.
>
> Would you reach for the peach behind you, please?
>
> That nasty thief stole my briefcase!
>
> My neighbor belongs to the Athletes' Club.

Part 6. Read Nonsense Words

Read each nonsense word aloud.

29. meep	**30.** reat	**31.** quee	**32.** zene
33. nief	**34.** panny	**35.** pheep	**36.** kiffy

Unit Checkpoint
Spellings for Sounds /ū/ and Long Double *o*

Part 1. Circle Words with Sound /ū/

Circle all the words that have the long *u* sound.

1. tooth   **2.** clue   **3.** cupid   **4.** mule

5. dusk   **6.** used   **7.** pool   **8.** student

Part 2. Circle Words with the Long Double *o* Sound

Circle all the words that have the long double *o* sound.

9. tooth   10. clue   11. cupid   12. mule

13. dusk   14. used   15. pool   16. student

Part 3. Many Spellings, One Sound: /ū/

Circle the four ways to spell the long *u* sound.

17. uu   **18.** u   **19.** ie   **20.** ue

21. oa   **22.** oo   **23.** u-e   **24.** ew

PHONICS

Part 4. Many Spellings, One Sound: Long Double *o* Sound

Circle the five ways to spell the long double o sound.

25. uu   **26.** u   **27.** ie   **28.** ue

29. oa   **30.** oo   **31.** u-e   **32.** ew

Part 5. Writing

Listen to each sentence. Repeat the sentence, and then write it.

33. _____

34. _____

35. _____

_____

Part 6. Read Aloud

Read the sentences aloud.

36.

Let's play music with our flutes and bugles.

The neighbors behind us will move next June.

Sue got glue on her new blue hat.

Both the moose and the goose need food.

Does that igloo have three bedrooms?

PHONICS

Unit Checkpoint
Spellings for Double *o* Sounds

Part 1. Circle Words with the Short Double *o* Sound

Circle all the words that have the short double *o* sound,
as in *book*.

1. shook   **2.** zoom   **3.** hook   **4.** wooden

5. foot   **6.** spoon   **7.** crooked   **8.** stood

PHONICS

Part 2. Circle Words with the Long Double *o* Sound

Circle all the words that have the long double o sound,
as in *doom*.

9. zoom   **10.** flute   **11.** new   **12.** cue

13. cute   **14.** broom   **15.** true   **16.** few

Part 3. Count Sounds

Count the number of sounds in the word, and write the number.

17. would ____   **18.** shook ____   **19.** hood ____

20. soon ____   **21.** tooth ____   **22.** spool ____

Part 4. Writing

Listen to the sentence. Repeat the sentence, and then write it.

23. _____

_____

24. _____

25. _____

_____

26. _____

Part 5. Read Aloud

Read the sentences aloud.

27.

Mom and I are about to go fishing in the brook.

Our neighborhood pool will open in June.

My newt grew a new tail once.

Sue is due to come home soon.

"Boo-hoo," said the cartoon cat.

Part 6. Read Sight Words

Read each sight word aloud.

28. come   **29.** behind   **30.** now   **31.** about

32. neighbor   **33.** against   **34.** once   **35.** every

Unit Checkpoint
Review Long Vowels and Double *o* Sounds

Part 1. Circle Words with the Short Double *o* Sound

Circle all the words that have the short double *o* sound, as in *book*.

1. hood   **2.** boom   **3.** brook   **4.** should

Part 2. Circle Words with the Long Double *o* Sound

Circle all the words that have the long double *o* sound, as in *school*.

5. shampoo   **6.** book   **7.** would   **8.** clue

9. crew   **10.** flute   **11.** cute   **12.** few

Part 3. Circle Words with Long Vowel Sounds

Circle all the words that have long vowel sounds.

13. main   **14.** crop   **15.** bead   **16.** flight

17. class   **18.** mow   **19.** could   **20.** menu

PHONICS

Part 4. Writing

Listen to the sentence. Repeat the sentence, and then write it.

21. _____

_____

22. _____

_____

23. _____

_____

Part 5. Read Aloud
Read the sentences aloud.

24.

The raccoon is behind the woodpile.

Please loop the string through the wooden hoop.

Feed the kangaroo, the goose, and the moose.

Jean is afraid her loose tooth will fall out too soon.

Mrs. Snow saw a new woolen coat she liked.

PHONICS

Part 6. Read Words

Read each word aloud.

25. toolbox	26. crooked	27. looked
28. hooted	29. party	30. seaweed
31. chief	32. hero	33. neighborhood
34. coaching	35. juggled	36. fudge

Part 7. Read Sight Words

Read each sight word aloud.

37. follow	38. saw	39. please
40. about	41. come	42. once
43. neighbor	44. every	

Unit Checkpoint
Sound /er/ Spelled −er, −ir, −ur, and −ear

Part 1. Circle Words with Sound /er/

Circle all the words that have the sound /er/.

1. curl   **2.** shirt   **3.** cusp   **4.** herd

5. blank   **6.** hard   **7.** fern   **8.** skirt

Part 2. Many Spellings, One Sound

Circle the four ways to spell the sound /er/.

9. are   10. er   11. ear

12. ir   13. oar   14. ur

Part 3. Read Sight Words

Read each sight word aloud.

15. please	**16.** follow	**17.** saw	**18.** once
19. about	**20.** come	**21.** behind	**22.** neighbor

Part 4. Writing

Listen to the sentence. Repeat the sentence, and then write it.

23. _____

24. _____

25. _____

Part 5. Read Aloud

Read the sentences aloud.

26.

Color the paper with your markers.

It's her birthday today.

She got dirt on her skirt.

Churn the butter until it is firm.

Badgers dig in the earth.

Part 6. Read Nonsense Words

Read each nonsense word aloud.

27. derm	**28.** virch	**29.** learp	**30.** pert
31. birm	**32.** lurd	**33.** surd	**34.** ner

Name

Date

Unit Checkpoint
Sound /ĕ/ Spelled *ea*

Part 1. Circle Words with Sound /ĕ/

Circle all the words that have the sound /ĕ/.

1. team
2. preach
3. bread
4. death
5. eat
6. instead
7. head
8. bean

Part 2. Count Sounds

Count the number of sounds in the word, and write the number.

9. bread ____   **10.** thread ____   **11.** health ____

12. dead ____   **13.** head ____   **14.** spread ____

PHONICS

Part 3. Read Sight Words

Read each sight word aloud.

15. under	**16.** everything	**17.** whether
18. please	**19.** follow	**20.** saw
21. come	**22.** about	

Part 4. Writing

Listen to the sentence. Repeat the sentence, and then write it.

23. _____

24. _____

25. _____

Part 5. Read Aloud

Read the sentences aloud.

26.

> She has a feather under her headband.
>
> I went to bed after I read my book.
>
> Good health is a wonderful gift.
>
> Spread butter on your cornbread.
>
> Everything, whether big or small, goes in the shed.

Part 6. Read Nonsense Words

Read each nonsense word aloud.

27. pight		**28.** barz		**29.** gort		**30.** perd
31. birm		**32.** lurd		**33.** faip		**34.** zoe

Unit Checkpoint
Sound /oi/ Spelled *oi* and *oy*

Part 1. Circle Words with Sound /oi/

Circle all the words that have the sound /oi/.

1. foil	**2.** coil	**3.** joy	**4.** fool
5. call	**6.** hoist	**7.** just	**8.** joint

Part 2. Count Sounds

Count the number of sounds in the word, and write the number.

9. boy _____ **10.** toy _____ **11.** Roy _____

12. join _____ **13.** coin _____ **14.** point _____

PHONICS

Part 3. Read Sight Words

Read each sight word aloud.

15. nothing	**16.** everything	**17.** under
18. almost	**19.** whether	**20.** over
21. please	**22.** saw	

Part 4. Writing

Listen to the sentence. Repeat the sentence, and then write it.

23. _____

24. _____

25. _____

Part 5. Read Aloud

Read the sentences aloud.

26.
> I almost had to start over.
>
> That noise will annoy Heather.
>
> Roy has nothing that can spoil.
>
> I will point to the best one.
>
> It was a joy to play with my toys.

Part 6. Read Nonsense Words

Read each nonsense word aloud.

27. doy	**28.** zoy	**29.** gloy	**30.** phoy
31. toin	**32.** droy	**33.** moid	**34.** zoich

Unit Checkpoint
Sound /aw/ Spelled *au* and *aw*

Part 1. Circle Words with Sound /aw/
Circle all the words that have the sound /aw/.

1. flawless   2. brawl   3. tent   4. lawn

5. because   6. lane   7. broil   8. taunt

PHONICS

Part 2. Count Sounds

Count the number of sounds in the word, and write the number.

9. draw _____   **10.** saw _____   **11.** claw _____

12. fawn _____   **13.** cause _____   **14.** Paul _____

Part 3. Read Sight Words

Read each sight word aloud.

15. almost	**16.** over	**17.** nothing
18. everything	**19.** under	**20.** whether
21. follow	**22.** please	

Part 4. Writing

Listen to the sentence. Repeat the sentence, and then write it.

23. _____

24. _____

25. _____

Part 5. Read Aloud

Read the sentences aloud.

26.

> I think he draws very well.
>
> Paul will fold the stack of laundry.
>
> You may find August to be too hot.
>
> A hawk has strong jaws and sharp claws.
>
> Will you pause for a while?

Part 6. Read Nonsense Words

Read each nonsense word aloud.

27. taw	28. zoy	29. tawb	30. phaud
31. shoice	32. baun	33. waw	34. vaw

Unit Checkpoint
Sound /ow/ Spelled *ou* and *ow*

Part 1. Circle Words with Sound /ow/
Circle all the words that have the sound /ow/.

1. could
2. hold
3. scout
4. owl

5. ton
6. two
7. clown
8. foul

Part 2. Count Sounds

Count the number of sounds in the word, and write the number.

9. shout _____   **10.** crowd _____   **11.** sound _____

12. town _____   **13.** loud _____   **14.** now _____

PHONICS

Part 3. Read Sight Words

Read each sight word aloud.

15. number	**16.** nothing	**17.** almost
18. children	**19.** write	**20.** over
21. under	**22.** whether	

Part 4. Writing

Listen to the sentence. Repeat the sentence, and then write it.

23. _____

24. _____

25. _____

Part 5. Read Aloud

Read the sentences aloud.

26. I will clean the children's spill with a towel.

    The brown kangaroo has a pouch for her baby.

    I'm about to write the number down.

    The clown will not frown when he tells a joke.

    Jim and Pete found out about trout in
    the stream.

Part 6. Read Words

Read each word aloud.

27. snout   **28.** owl   **29.** found   **30.** clown

---

31. couch   **32.** gown   **33.** about   **34.** tower

Name ___ Date ___

Unit Checkpoint
Sound /ō/ Spelled *ow*

Part 1. Circle Words with Sound /ō/

Circle all the words that have the sound /ō/.

1. clown
2. shown
3. loud
4. lawn
5. how
6. blow
7. crow
8. stow

PHONICS

LANGUAGE ARTS GREEN | SOUND /ō/ SPELLED *ow*   PH 211

Part 2. Count Sounds

Count the number of sounds in the word, and write the number.

9. crown _____ **10.** low _____ **11.** brown _____

12. how _____ **13.** thrown _____ **14.** grow _____

Part 3. Read Sight Words

Read each sight word aloud.

15. first   **16.** number   **17.** write

18. children   **19.** its   **20.** because

21. please   **22.** while

PHONICS

Part 4. Writing

Listen to the sentence. Repeat the sentence, and then write it.

23. _____

_____

24. _____

25. _____

_____

Part 5. Read Aloud

Read the sentences aloud.

26.

> My shadow will grow because the sun gets lower.
>
> The first boat rows quickly down the river.
>
> The catcher throws the ball to the pitcher's mound.
>
> The owl and the crow will fly into the tower tonight.
>
> The brown bowl is below the window.

> ## Part 6. Read Words
> Read each word aloud.

27. chowder   28. mellow   29. shown

30. shower   31. blown   32. downtown

33. crowbar   34. glow